Table of Contents

Introduction

Special Bonus For You

Chapter 1: What Are The Seven Steps To Self-Healing?

Chapter 2: Self-Healing With Meditation

Chapter 3: Positive Thinking and Self-Healing

Chapter 4: 5 Ways to getting Rid of Toxins in Your Body

Chapter 5: How to Declutter Your Mind

Chapter 6: Eating For Health in Self-Healing and Development

Chapter 7: Aromatherapy in Self-Healing and Development

Chapter 8: Yoga Practice For Self-Healing and Development

Chapter 9: Your Body is Self-Healing

Chapter 10: Self-Healing in our Daily Life

Chapter 11: Heal Physically and Emotionally

Chapter 12: Self-Healing and Group Healing With Reiki

Conclusion

Check Out Other Books

Special Bonus For You

2op.

Introduction

As western medicine advances, more and more people forget their natural ability to promote their self-healing. Self-healing is a concept that has been practiced for tens of thousands of years in every ancient civilization from China to Mesopotamia to Greece to the Aborigines and Native Americans. While western medicine has many upsides, one of the biggest problems is that it counts on medicines, therapies, and surgeries to put a Band-Aid on problems instead of helping patients access their inner power for self-healing.

Self-healing comes in many forms, and this chapter will discuss a few of them. The first form of self-healing comes in the form of meditation. Meditation is good for the body in so many ways when you are healthy, but it is especially important when you are suffering from an illness or injury. It helps to relieve stress and promotes relaxation by calming your mind. Our heads are filled with thousands of thoughts daily - most of them full of worry and stress. When we meditate, it helps to calm our mind and our body so that it can release stress from the cells and begin its natural process of healing. If the body is full of negative energy created by our thoughts, then it cannot access the positive energy power to self-heal. Meditation helps us to release the negativity that builds up throughout the day so that our body can reenergize and rejuvenate.

Another form of self-healing comes in the ancient forms of martial arts like tai chi and qigong. Their efficiency to promote self-healing is that the gentle movements combined with deep breathing bring much-needed oxygen to the muscles. Oxygen has tremendous healing properties, and our muscles and organs rarely get all the oxygen they need - this is because as a species we have developed a habit of frequent shallow breathing, instead of the deep, nourishing breaths that deliver oxygen deep into the cells. When we take shallow breathes we only take in a small amount of oxygen that is quickly used up by the body for the brain and vital organs, leaving very little left over for our other cells, muscles, and organs. The deep breathing and gentle muscle movements of tai chi and qigong take in massive amounts of oxygen into our system while the gentle movements promote deliverance of that oxygen to the cells and muscles groups.

If western medicine is not working for you or you want to avoid the entire prescriptions, then look towards self-healing. Whether you are interested in self-healing for the common everyday cold or a more serious illness or injury, look towards meditation and the softer forms of ancient martial arts. They will not only help your body relax, reduce stress and dispel negative energy from your body, but they will also promote healing by delivering healing oxygen deep into your cells where it can begin to repair the damage caused by stress and illness.

Chapter 1: What Are The Seven Steps To Self-Healing?

Step 1 - Learning How to Properly Relax

To re-program your subconscious mind you have to learn to relax properly.

The audio relaxation exercise which accompanies the first of the seven steps to self-healing helps you to relax properly. It also advances an idea of having your special Workshop (which is your creative mind) to help you solve problems in every aspect of your life.

It shows how to carry out a very powerful breathing exercise.

This is the first, and most important step in gaining self-healing and self-awareness. We recommend that you use this relaxation and circulation technique as you study the self-healing and self-awareness concepts.

Rhythmic Breathing

Avoid breathing too deeply at first, or holding your breath too long - All effort should be gentle and easy - The aim is to establish a rhythm.

Simply relax - Do not try to follow the words - Do not try too hard - Just relax and drift along with the words and music.

Do not worry if you fall asleep during this exercise, the words and healing are directed at your subconscious mind.

Use this relaxation and breathing exercise to begin your inner journey to the deepest levels of yourself.

Steps 2 to 7: Gradually and gently take you to higher and higher energy vibrations.

We have designed a special healing symbol we call "The Spinning Cross" which visually activates the deepest levels of your subconscious mind to that state of self-awareness where some very positive changes can start to be made to your spirit, emotions, mind, and body.

It is used as a type of Stargate in lessons 2 to 7 to raise your vibrations above the struggles and difficulties of your present karmic state of existence to the harmony and peace of the approaching UNITY with the deepest subconscious levels of yourself.

This is done in step by step manner, with each successive lesson lifting you higher and higher out of the low vibrations of sickness and worry and into the higher energy vibrations of health and well-being.

Step 2 - Taking Back Your Power

Let all parts of yourself be re-absorbed into yourself. Over your lifetime you have probably given away your power to many people.

Now is the time to take back your power again. Allow all the parts of yourself that you feel have been missing for you to come back into your body, mind, emotions, and spirit.

Step 3 - Anger And Cruelty

Now is the time to finally let go of all the damaging effects that anger and cruelty have caused in you. Allow all the peace and harmony to come back into your body, mind, emotions, and spirit.

Step 4 - Fear, Lack And The Abuse Of Power

Now is the time to finally let go of all the damaging effects that this fear, lack and the abuse of power has caused in you. Allow all the peace and harmony to come back into your body, mind, emotions, and spirit.

Step 5 - Unreachable Goals, Ethics And Morals, False Expectations And Identifications.

Now is the time to finally let go of all the damaging effects that this fear, unreachable goals, ethics and morals, as well as false expectations and identifications have caused in you. Allow all the peace and harmony to come back into your body, mind, emotions, and spirit.

Step 6 - Religious And Spiritual Desire

Now is the time to finally let go of all the damaging effects that this excessive religious and spiritual desire has caused in you. Allow all the peace and harmony to come back into your body, mind, emotions, and spirit.

Step 7 - Judgement, Self Love, And Forgiveness

Now is the time to finally let go of all the damaging effects that this excessive judgment, lack of self-love and forgiveness has caused in you. Allow all the Peace and Harmony to come back into your body, mind, emotions, and spirit.

Chapter 2: Self-Healing With Meditation

To overcome it, now, a lot of medicine and pharmacy technology has been developing from traditional till super sophisticated. But, new various diseases still come and make new problem in the community. Medicine and pharmacy technology, not fully can solve and cure those problems. Moreover, if you consider side effect from its healing approach.

Meditation has been considering as a healing therapy for a long time ago. It is a healing and medicine alternative by a human in the various side of the world. This chapter discusses how to self-healing with meditation simply.

What is Self-healing with Meditation?

Everybody can heal their self with many approaches. For example, if you feel pain, you can buy the drug in a drug store without a medical recipe.

Another way is made a self-healing process with meditation. Meditation can use for single alternative healing process or supplemental for the main healing process. Self-healing is a healing process with our energy, our mind, our desire and our pray to heal our illness. Meditation is a tool to develop energy to heal our illness and more health and fresh our condition.

Various meditations can develop your energy to heal our health problems. In meditation, energy awakens in our body and makes healing process automatically. When you are in a relaxed condition, your energy will improve your quality body and soul.

Which illness can heal by Meditation?

All kind of illness can heal through meditation. It can be directly healed or need long time process to heal an illness. For examples: kinds of illness are a head pain, nerve pain, stress, hypertension, stroke, psychosomatics, leukemia, tiredness, anemia, back pain, cardiovascular, and many more.

All kind of illness can be solved by meditation because our energy and pray will make healing process. For light illness, we can easily heal by meditation in very fast time. My experiences showed some people with common urban problem like head pain, tiredness, stress and back problem, such light pain can be easily healed with meditation.

A Simple Method

Below are some simple methods when you have pain:

1. Stand Up Meditation. If you can stand up, please stand up freely on the floor. But if you are having difficulty to stand up due to your illness, then get somebody to help you stand up. You can stand up leaning against the wall. Close your eyes and feel the energy move from earth to all your body and soul. Do not forget to pray for your way. Do this with arranging your breath for any time (15-20 minutes). Our experience showed a woman who suffers leukemia could heal with this method. Other pains will be easier to heal.

2. Sit down meditation. Do this like the abovementioned but in sit down position. You can try another position too but do not push yourself in hard position. That position must be easy to use.

Chapter 3: Positive Thinking and Self-Healing

Healing without using any medicine sounds incredulous. Most of us are skeptics who view medicine as the ultimate cure for any ailment or disease.

Our parents, friends, doctors, and media have programmed our minds to think that what our bodies need are pills to pop that fix practically anything from a bum stomach to depression.

There is, however, another form of healing that works for many, and which doesn't include taking pills. And it starts with your mind.

Gravity, radio frequency and magnetic force are examples. Quantum physicists confirm the energy that the human brain emits. When we think and feel, our brains give off energy at a particular frequency. Brain waves can be measured electronically.

In fact, brain activity is often used as an indication of life. Doctors can detect when someone is mentally "alive" by monitoring brain activity. When a person's brain registers a flat line, he may be pronounced "legally dead" in some jurisdictions. That is how important the mind is.

Placebo effect

Most of the time, you think automatically. You think as a result of how your mind has been programmed.

For example, if you think that the pill you are swallowing is the cure for migraine, the chances are that your headache will go away.

The pharmacological effects of the medicine may have caused the cure, but some studies show how people experience healing after taking non-pharmacological substances or a placebo. This is the famous "placebo effect."

The placebo effect confirms that the human body can heal itself without medicine, and by simply using the mind's thinking power.

To use positive thinking to heal yourself you need to start believing that you are healed.

Positive thinking

Stress with a negative thought that goes unchecked. Someone who tends to linger on the negatives leaves himself susceptible to stress.

Eventually, stress is manifested by headaches, an upset stomach or worse, by a fatal illness. If stress starts with a negative thought, then to eliminate it, you need to replace those thoughts with more positive ones.

Listen to good music, read an inspiring book, or learn how to revert to thinking happy thoughts.

Laughter is still the best medicine.

Most of us find it hard to get past our problems that are sources of stress.

Instead of letting negative thoughts sink our bodies deeper into sickness, try turning your attention to something funny and laugh at it. Watch funny movies and share jokes with friends.

Laughter is the easiest way to get rid of negative thoughts. When you laugh, your mind is distracted from your problems and focused on more positive thoughts. When you laugh, you not only feel good but you help yourself heal.

Thus, many have included laughter as an essential part of their healing process. When someone you know is feeling poorly or down, offer something to make that person laughs. By doing so, you might just help them get well.

Chapter 4: 5 Ways to getting Rid of Toxins in Your Body

The number one cause of almost all of today's diseases and common ailments are these toxins. Therefore, it is important that you get rid of these toxins in your body so that you can enjoy a long and healthy life.

Living Foods

One of the best and least painful ways is just to change your diet to a living foods diet. This means that all your foods should come from a plant, and should be raw, with all of its enzymes still alive. You do not have to make the change overnight, but you should make gradual changes that you can stick with so that over time you can become 100% raw.

Fasting

Fasting is a quick way for you to detoxify as it requires that you do not eat for a certain period. The longer you fast, the more toxins will be eliminated. However, fasting can be hard on the body and should only be done under close guidance when doing it for the first time.

Juice fasting for a day or two is suitable for those who have never fasted before. But for those who are comfortable with fasting can fast for as long as 30 days, and may even consider doing water fasts as well. You should always listen to your body and stop fasting when it tells you to.

Saunas and Hot Baths

Saunas and hot baths are another great way for you to detoxify, as they help you to sweat out the toxins through your skin. The longer you can stay in these the more beneficial they will be. Just remember to drink plenty of fluids to restore the fluids lost from the sweating.

Colon Cleanse

Your colon is your large intestine where the most toxins tend to build up. Thus, a colon cleanse can help you to eliminate lots of toxins fast. However, you should do your research on these as there are methods which your body can become dependent on. Try to go natural whenever possible.

Weight Loss

An overweight person will be required to lose excess weight, and the toxins will begin to leave your body. You can do this by reducing calories and eating lots of leafy vegetables, nuts or fresh fruits.

Chapter 5: How to Declutter Your Mind

Every day we are bombarded with things, some of these things are important, and some just aren't. Let's choose a better word, situations. However, the challenge comes when we put a higher level of importance in some situations that aren't that important. Such situations then become distractions away from those things/situations we really ought to be focusing on. That's right; they take your mind on a path away from what is important to you without you realizing.

Do you sometimes or perhaps often feel your mind is filled with all this information, imprints and ideas and you simply can't find a way to create order or gain control over it again? When you experienced this as well, I can comfort you, most people are dealing with this, every day.

So here are 7 quick ways to stay focus and declutter your mind:

1. Prioritize

Take a few minutes be it 15 - 30 minutes every night before bed or even in the morning after waking to set out the tasks you want to accomplish. Assign a level of priority to each and carry them out in the order of most important first down to the least important. If new tasks come up as you go through the day, then see where they fall into your other priorities for the day.

2. Stay Calm

Yes, it may be hard to stay calm when things seem to be going crazy. But worrying does more harm than good. Think about it, how much have you gotten accomplished while you were worrying. Chances are not that much. So don't clutter your mind with situations you have no control over, because, you have no control over them.

3. Stay Positive

Yup, keep a positive outlook on life does help with decluttering your mind. It links back to help you stay calm. You can stay positive and keep your mind free of clutter by reading what benefits you and not the latest gossip column. Keep positive people in your circle of friends and negative people at a distance.

4. Be Grateful

If you are reading this chapter, then electricity is one to be thankful for. Overall, being thankful for the good that has happened to you in your life goes a long way towards just helping you feel better and decluttering your mind. Why? Well, you don't spend time wanting this and that. Instead let's start being thankful and see how it goes.

5. Be Real

Yes, being genuine is a great way to declutter your mind as you don't spend energy being anxious all the time worrying about how to impress people. Besides you might be amazed at how much people might like and respect what you are.

6. Forgive and Forget

This helps keep you in a positive state. Might not be the easiest of things to do but at least you can begin to heal. Some say keeping a grudge is like drinking poison and expecting the other person to die. It just doesn't work, so let go of the anger and pain.

7. Get it Done

Take action now. Do something that gets you closer towards your goals and being able to tick off the items you plan for yourself to accomplish.

Chapter 6: Eating For Health in Self-Healing and Development

Food is very important to our body as it enables it to function properly as well as heal itself if need be. A person eating a well-balanced diet will find fighting infection easier than a person who is eating the wrong kind of foods.

Food can even affect our mood and how we relate to others. Certain foods aid in alleviating certain problems. Take someone who is suffering from lack of sleep if he/she drinks warm milk just before going to bed it would help them go to sleep. Also avoiding drinks with caffeine such as coffee would be a wise idea.

Eating oneself to good health requires making a conscious decision on what and how one eats. Take the obesity levels that are gripping the world today. That stems partly from how our utensils have got bigger over time, as well as all the super-sizing that is going on. While one could wonder what our plates have to do with it. Over time, the cups, as well as glasses, have increased in volume and hence we have just consumed much more with it. If you put smaller plates on a buffet table, it is proven that people tend to eat significantly less. If you alter the type of plates in your home, you would then eat less, and that is a significant key to health. The idea of eating in moderation is a concept most people seem to have not grasped and with most people, excess drives everything.

In line with our consumer-driven society where everyone wants more, bigger things, portions have followed suit, and our collective weight bears testament to our eating habits. This YOYO diet causes many people to fail to diet. It causes people to fluctuate in weight, and it is not ideal. Eating moderate quantities would be a better alternative. It is important to eat moderate quantities but what is equally as important is eating the right foods in a balanced diet.

Being aware of what you put in your body is important. When you start thinking about what exactly you are eating, is it organic, is it live food, or is it processed food? If it is processed can you even pronounce the list of contents? Are those things good for you? It is then that you find out exactly what goes into that food.

Eating the right kind of food will aid in your self-development as some fish oils have been linked with good brain function so adding them to your diet would be a beneficial thing.

Food should be enjoyed and cherished, after all, without it, we would not be able to keep our body running.

Chapter 7: Aromatherapy in Self-Healing and Development

Aromatherapy is a wonderful way to reduce stress, calm yourself or even help fire up your brain for busy work days. You can use aromatherapy as a natural sleep aid. It can help relieve minor symptoms of depression. It can relieve both stress and pain at the same time. When you relieve pain, relaxation will become easier for you and give you the peace you're looking for.

Aromatherapy can provide those deeper levels of relaxation that people on self-development and self-healing path are looking for. Everyone has difficult, stressful days that are hard to let go of. Using aromatherapy as part of your daily relaxation practice will make letting go easier, and help you to perform to the best of your abilities.

By relieving stress, you'll begin to develop the confidence needed to expand new skills and to create your life consciously. Remember stress is not the natural order of things. We have to go through a lot of extra work to be in a state of stress. We have just forgotten our natural state and how to get back to it.

Aromatherapy uses essential oils in bath oils, lotions or diffusers to apply the oils for maximum benefit. You may benefit from contacting an aroma therapist to help you in choosing the best oils for you. They can also mix up special blends.

The popular oils along with their healing properties are:

Peppermint: Headaches, indigestion

Eucalyptus: Colds, muscle tension

Ylang Ylang: Promotes relaxation

Lavender: Relaxing, treats minor burns

Lemon: Uplifting, treat infections, deodorizing

Clary Sage: Painkiller, balances hormones

Roman Chamomile: Relaxing, relieves insomnia

Tea Tree: Treats a variety of fungal infections

Rosemary: Mental stimulant, immune system stimulant

If you suffer from insomnia, you can mist your pillowcase before you sleep, and it will help you with your sweet dreams. Sandalwood can help you relax into your daily meditation easier. Just remember not to overdo it. A little will go a long way in helping you relax.

Be sure to read all labels before using your aromatherapy as a guide to self-healing and development. Oils are very strong and can be dangerous if not used as instructed on the bottle. A competent aromatherapist or your physician should be able to help you use your essential oils in the most beneficial way possible for you.

Chapter 8: Yoga Practice For Self-Healing and Development

"Yoga" means union. It is poses meant to stretch your muscles, focus on breathing and help you experience balance in your life. A daily yoga practice not only adds flexibility to your body but helps to promote relaxation and a feeling of confidence. It creates a space for your mind, body, and spirit to unite and work together consciously.

There isn't anyone, young or old, who couldn't benefit from a regular yoga practice. Practicing the postures that compose a yoga routine isn't about forcing your body into a pose. Rather it is about listening to your body's inner wisdom and allowing it do what it can do at that moment. If you practice regularly, you will see an increase in your flexibility and energy.

People who practice yoga frequently have reported some positive side effects, such as:

- Feeling invigorated after a session - Stronger and more toned body - Boosts energy levels naturally - Lower blood pressure - Can relieve depression and anxiety - Improved digestion and circulation - Relief from the symptoms of arthritis

Their knees start to wobble, and before you know it, they are tongue-tied and cannot speak. Yoga offers techniques which can not only help you calm yourself but as you practise Yoga, you will learn how to control your fear and do things you previously thought were impossible for you.

Do you find yourself wiped out at the end of a day from all the stress at work? If you do, give yourself a great gift by joining a yoga class. With the popularity of yoga increasing, you should be able to find a studio that is on your way home from work.

Another way to practice yoga is right in the comfort and privacy of your own home. Go to your local bookstore, stop at a yard sale or go to your public library. DVDs are available to teach you yoga postures on your TV. The library may even have them available for free. You will be so proud of yourself and feel like a new person when you take the time to learn yoga.

Using yoga as one of your regular practices will move your self-growth to a whole new level. You will feel and become the new person that you want to be and can be proud of.

Chapter 9: Your Body is Self-Healing

Your body is self-healing. Consider a broken bone. If you break a bone, a doctor doesn't heal it; he will set it then put a cast on it. You are then given medicine to ward off infection and to kill the pain. But your body heals the bone by mending it. You must supply the nutrition that it uses to do this.

Your body can heal a scratch, a cut, a burn and even a cold or flu. Medications taken for these problems are used to help kill bacteria and to make you more comfortable.

Our lymphatic system is filled with t-cells, macrophages, and many white blood cells to help kill bacteria, viruses and neutralize toxins. This is our immune system and is evidence that the body is self-healing.

Problems arise when our immune system becomes either weak or attacks itself. Constant inflammation from chemicals, drugs and other environmental toxins over-burden and overwhelm our systems. This, in turn, can lead to chronic disease

When we eat junk food or overeat foods such as meat and bread, it doesn't get digested and removed efficiently. It becomes toxic, so our body's response is to defend itself by excreting extra mucus in the small intestine. When this happens repeatedly, the mucus builds up with the partially digested food, and now we have a buildup of waste or a plaque lining.

This is why colon cleansing and detoxing are so important. As we take responsibility for our health and ease the burden on the body, our immune system becomes free to work as it should.

Some doctors will tell you that while the body is self-healing, it is also meant to detox or cleanse itself - and it is. However, your organs of elimination cannot work properly if they are overloaded. As the buildup makes the body sluggish, the liver and gallbladder cannot dump the bile and waste because is nowhere to send it to.

Normally, much of this toxic bile and waste would be sent to the small intestine, the colon then out. But if the small intestine is partially blocked while at the same time being bombarded on a regular basis with over-eating, junk food or more chemicals, it slows down. There is simply no place to "dump" the waste. As this waste accumulates, your body must now focus all attention on keeping you alive. If it must do this in a state of sickness, it will.

It's much like this; if you set your hand on a table and pour a little dirt on it, you will pick up your hand and shake it off. But if you put 10 pounds of dirt on your hand, then you need help removing it. There is nothing wrong with your hand, but you need to get the weight off if you want full use of it.

Our organs and immune system are very strong when we are young. But as the years go on toxins do accumulate. If you want full use of your body and its healing abilities, you must help it clears the old waste and build-up. When you accomplish this, you will find that the body is self-healing and you are stronger than you may have previously thought.

Chapter 10: Self-Healing in our Daily Life

In our daily life we come across our up and downs; we love the ups but not the downs. We can always boost our egos when positive things happen since we can get over-excited or become grateful. On the other hand, we can either calm ourselves to look at the bigger picture or get very upset and involve ourselves in our drama when we come across negative things. The experience brings the wisdom, and the best experience can come when we have a basic understanding of the power of self-healing and hence the difference between choosing each path is our wisdom and experience in dealing with situations.

It is essential to understand how the law of attractions works when we want to know more about the power of healing. We will always attract the bad and good events into our lives since we are responsible for the creation of our realities whether we like it or not. This gets understood better when we get to experience in applying self-healing but to start, sciences such as quantum physics has proven how particles behave according to the observer.

We can see when we are doing well for ourselves when we attract the right moments in our lives and then feel energized as a result when we use the law of attraction as our guide. When we are attracting negative events, it only means we need to work on ourselves, and that's when we need to know how to self-heal hence the challenge becomes to learn how to channel this energy. Even a very well-balanced person will attract negative events, we all have issues to work on, it is the purpose of why we are here!

We can turn things around to gain strength and positive energy out of it when we can take responsibility for a negative event and see what it is we need to heal. Surrendering our defenses and our ego when we feel pain from a certain event is the first step to doing so. We then need to feel the pain and confront it with our emotions, which in turn will bring a lot of energy to our consciousness where we can see everything on a clearer level. Going further with this, we can let go of our fears if we are ready. When we succeed, even partially, we can feel a relief along with a sense of clarity and power. When we can fully heal ourselves, we will no longer attract certain kinds of negative events in our lives.

We can see the power we bring to ourselves, and it will get addictive as we heal ourselves through our negative events. We therefore need to take the time to step back and focus on ourselves instead of reacting with our egos, even if the reaction is internal. When we learn from ourselves, we gain a lot of wisdom and even compassion towards others who may be going through same issues we had.

When we trail innermost intentions to get ourselves healed we align ourselves with a higher purpose. This is when we can start seeing how the law of attraction will assist us to take it to the next level. Our energy vibration rises when we connect more with the world around us and brings more purposeful events to guide us through self-healing. It is very exciting when we recognize them because we feel that we are connecting ourselves to a larger world since they are events of synchronicity.

Handling the excitement is our next challenge. It always comes in the form of commanding energy most often it will be irresistible, hence we give reward to ourselves through boosting our ego. But the problem here becomes whatever goes up must come down. Our energy always changes when we get ourselves into ego boost where the events of synchronicity will slow down. The purpose we certainly get into an ego boost is that we also have issues to work out on this end, where ego is a result of overwhelming the uncertainties we may have. Mindfulness is needed in this part where being aware of our ego is important.

We always attract our problems, and we need to heal what's inside to stop the vicious circles. Integrating self-healing into our daily lives is not only beneficial but even necessary if we want to grow free of our problems. That sounds boring but not when we start to see the benefits and the steps into a new reality. It's all about the realities that we let ourselves live in, and we have the power to change them.

The one aspect that we all want more of is love if we can focus on that and grow it, everything else we do will be even better. It is a simple mindset that we can apply to every aspect of our lives, and when we do, we will have more success in everything we do. It is also our source of power as well as our connection to a divine universe. You cannot search for love since it is a natural energy in us that wants to come out, but it is controlled by our obstructions which need to be healed!

Chapter 11: Heal Physically and Emotionally

Whether you need to physically or emotionally heal yourself, you will be interested in learning and begin implementing various self-healing techniques. Some healing techniques are ideal for preventing or curing sickness while others get rid of chronic pain. If you are emotionally hurt, there are things you can do to relax your mind and body to achieve a better sense of peace than any medication could grant you. Consider these specific healing options for both physical and emotional ailments.

Physically, the first self-healing technique is massage. You know the precise areas in your feet that are killing you. The same is true of your hands, your neck, and other areas of the body that you can easily reach. Also, using a loofah to massage your skin in the shower can do wonders for promoting healthy skin and easing fatigue. Then, there is yoga. This stretching, flexibility-promoting exercise is great for both your body and your mind. Eliminate chronic back pain with certain beneficial stretches and work your way gently to stretch out and repair tight or damaged muscles. Breath work is the final physical healing technique that allows you to release negative energy to reduce migraines, help with insomnia, and stimulate the organs.

Emotionally, there is a great deal you can do for healing as well. Positive affirmation is all about turning negative emotions and thoughts into positive ones to boost your self-esteem. The repetition of positive affirmations to yourself, you can change the way you think and feel about yourself and any situation. This is also called mind over matter. Then, you cannot underestimate the healing power of music. Sound healing works because certain rhythms and pitches affect your limbic system, which is the center for emotion in the brain. Certain kinds of music have a profound way of nourishing the soul. Aromatherapy is another technique that affects people mostly emotionally, but physically as well. Essential oils are used to create a therapeutic atmosphere of aroma that can stimulate the brain and be inhaled into the lungs for beneficial effects there as well.

These and many other self-healing techniques can and should be utilized by anyone who needs an emotional or physical pick-me-up. While these techniques are safe, you should exercise caution in aspects of yoga and aromatherapy to make sure you perform them correctly. Also, do not attempt self-diagnose or to treat any serious condition without consulting a doctor.

Chapter 12: Self-Healing and Group Healing With Reiki

Reiki healing has been practiced for several years now. Reiki healing is comprehensive. It can be applied to the spirit, the mind, and the body with the intention to achieve balance in every aspect of a person's life. Reiki can also help in enhancing the personal abilities and talents of an individual. In short, it brings out the good in you so you can have an improved life experience. This benefits not only you but those around you as well.

To take advantage of the benefits of this magnificent healing art, you must decide to get attuned to this sacred practice. This sacred covenant has to be received, learned, and nurtured throughout life.

Self-Healing

To tap into this magnificent Life Force and rip the benefits of this energy, you must learn the Reiki healing process in depth, and commit to practice and incorporate the art to your day to day routine. You will be learning different techniques, and with practice and time, you will come to master them. The more you commit to this practice the closer you will be to your physical well-being or personal development goal.

Part of learning Reiki involves acquiring the know-how to practice self-healing. When you learn to perform self-healing, the technique will vary a bit because the hand positions will be different to those you use when healing others. Once you learn this, you will be able to heal yourself effectively. Once you become proficient, you may even develop your personalized healing system by positioning your hands in places that create the most comfort which will eventually work to your advantage. In any case, when you commit to mind, heart, and spirit to learn Reiki, you will succeed for sure.

Taking the time for Self-Healing

Once you learn the basics to perform a Reiki session on yourself, you will have to allocate at least 30 minutes of time for this purpose on a regular basis. In this allotted time, you will concentrate your efforts and intention on just the Reiki process. It is of the outmost importance to learn to value yourself and your overall well-being, so you must dedicate this time fully and only to your self-healing.

You will have the choice to use either the scanning technique or the hand positions as your technique. Your focus should be on the areas that require the most healing. When the session begins, let go of worry and concern of your daily life so you can be gently guided as to where your hands should be placed and which area of your body should be touched or focused on. You must be focused at the moment and concentrate on the energy while you're performing Reiki on yourself.

Allow for the energy to flow and feel its vibration. While the session is going on, contemplate your daily activities from a distance and then observe where your life is heading from a detached perspective, as if you were watching a movie. It is by this means of observing your life that your self-healing will have the best results. This technique helps promote the development of a healthy attitude in life which will eventually have a great impact in your life. More so, this self-reflection technique will not only heal your physical body but bring about creative ideas to give you insight on how to best handle your problems.

Self-Healing in Groups

Reiki is powerful not only when practiced on oneself but with others and in groups. There is a special synergy when practiced in a group. You may want to explore the benefits of a group session, and if you know other healers, you may want to invite them to perform a session together. This practice is very effective because you won't only get to heal yourself but you will be placing your focus on helping others heal which can work wonders for all involved. In many instances, it's been found that people heal faster when doing sessions in a group setting. This is because of the mass concentration that draws powerful energy to heal each other. Sometimes, even complete individual healing will materialize. The secret lies in the sharing of energy and the support that is present as the group gets on with the session.

As an added benefit, when you practice in a group you have the opportunity to discuss with your peers your challenges and the areas of your life that need to be healed. If you find the group practice appealing, it is recommended to do it once per week to generate a more serious individual focus and a deeper collective purpose. Remember, the power is in the collective energy, so make sure your peers are committed as well.

Conclusion

Self-healing is a concept that is big in the holistic healing community as well as the energetic healing world. It is helpful, and a good addition to your toolbox for your abilities to influence your life positively, but it is not required.

For self-healing on a holistic healing level in your life, it is about tackling the issues from a mind body spirit level. Let us start with the mind concepts. For example, you are working on a love relationship issue in your life, and you need to work on self-healing. You have first to notice where the problems reside in the love issue along with your issues for this to be truly understood and to be resolved. You have to love yourself first. You have to embrace yourself, all aspect, even the ones you think aren't positive or altering, and accept everything about yourself.

For the body aspect, you can start, if you have been attuned to an energy form for healing, start sending self-healing to your physical body as well as your love issue you want to tackle. It is a two-step process. If you haven't been accustomed to any form of energy, you can still self-heal this way. Sit in a quiet room, calm your mind and body, and start to breathe deep. Focus on your breathing and slow this down. Place your hands on top of your thighs and just focus your body and concentrate on your breathing. This will calm down your energetic fields within your physical body and will slow them down to start their self-healing process.

For the spirit aspect, you can work on things such as meditating for yourself and your love issue. Begin managing a record and write all of the things you want to focus on for yourself and your love issue for your self-healing. If you prefer prayer, you can work with praying instead of meditating.

Self-healing is about focusing on your body from all levels and in all ways. It is not just one way is right, and the other is wrong, but a total comprehensive way to focus on yourself, your healing, and the areas that are concerning you today!

-- Elizabeth Caroline